Dedicated to all the
wonderful nannies who take such
great care of the next generation.

To:_____

From:_____

First Published 2023

Copyright © Gabriella Sellers Amy Weston

Published under licence by Brown Dog Books,
10b Greenway Farm, Bath Rd, Wick, nr. Bath, BS30 5RL

ISBN printed book: 978-1-83952-734-0

Printed & Bound in the UK

Cover and internal design by Gareth Williams

This book is printed on FSC®certified paper

FSC
www.fsc.org

MIX
Paper | Supporting
responsible forestry
FSC® C013604

MY NANNY AND ME

When it's time to say goodbye

Words by
Gabriella Sellers and
Amy Weston

Pictures by
Gareth Williams

Oh what fun we've had on our ADVENTURES together, From blowing BUBBLES, reading books, and chasing every FEATHER.

We've shared our STORY, both you and I, But there are times in life where we have to say GOODBYE.

What is your favourite memory from the time we have spent together?

In every story there are chapters,
Some with PIRATES, some with diggers and maybe
some with VELOCIRAPTORS!

Can you think of three
things we have learned
together?

Our story is just the same, with a CHAPTER next in line, Although this one is special as yours is different to MINE.

For now is the time that we move on,
One day I'll be here, and the next I'll be GONE.

You might feel SCARED, perhaps confused, or a tiny bit blue, But that's okay, tell me your FEELINGS and I'll help you through.

Change is EXCITING, see it as an adventure, as I will too, I wonder what MEMORIES you'll make and the things you'll do.

For this is not the END of the story, just the start of something NEW.

What are you most looking forward to in the next chapter?

GABRIELLA

Gabriella was raised in Devon and now lives in South West London with her husband Andy and their two sons Jonty and Lando. She loves to draw from personal experience when writing books and poetry. Gabriella has a keen interest in responsive parenting, which is the foundation of this book.

This book is a collaboration between Gabriella and Amy, who has nannied for the family for three years and counting.

AMY

Amy is a South Londoner born and raised, and the eldest of six children. She has devoted her life to nannying, and is passionate about supporting children through their emotions and ensuring they are heard.

My Nanny and Me is a passion project close to her heart, having left families in the past without any resources to support the emotional transition. Her mission is to help other families and nannies around the world have a positive experience.

Whilst not nannying, Amy can be found fishing, being outdoors and enjoying life to the fullest.

GARETH

Gareth lives in East London, with his amazing wife. From an early age he's loved to draw and doodle and that passion continues to this day. It's something he still can't believe he gets to do for a living!

He's worked on a wide range of published titles and has worked on a various other illustration projects that include greeting cards, editorial and Animation.

Gabriella

Amy

Gareth

AMY'S TOP TIPS FOR NANNIES AND PARENTS

It is easy and natural to want to protect our children from sadness, however, I believe that allowing all emotions to be shared and accepted will encourage a better relationship with feelings, both now and in the future.

To help with the tricky transition, here are some tips for both nannies and parents which I have collated over my time as a nanny:

1. Ensure both parents and nanny use the same reason and language to explain why the nanny is leaving. For example 'I will be looking after new babies now that you are ready for school'. Keeping the reason clear and concise will reduce confusion.

2. It's not their fault! Some children may think the nanny leaving is their fault, which of course it is not. Make this clear as part of the reason why the nanny is leaving.

3. Allow enough time to let them know what's happening. I recommend between 2-4 weeks to allow time to process what is happening, reinforce the message in a gentle way, and for both the nanny and parents to support emotions along the way.

4. Create a memory/scrap book of all your adventures together to give as a leaving present. I have found that children love looking back at all the things we have done and friends we have made.

5. Both nannies and parents need to appreciate the enormity of the change. I have often seen a period of 'mourning' from children, especially where there is a strong bond. Being honest, supportive, and positive about the future will help with the transition.

6. Whilst it's tempting to see the children soon after leaving, I recommend a period of time where you don't make contact. This allows them to get used to a new routine or nanny, and removes any confusion as to whether you might be coming back.

Remember this is not the end, just the start of something new!

SCRAPBOOK

STICK YOUR
PICTURES HERE

SCRAPBOOK

STICK YOUR
PICTURES HERE

Remember this is not the
end, just the start of
something new!